**Write Away**

# SOURCEBOOK

Practice Workshops,
Minilessons, and Daily Sentences

. . . a resource of student workshops,
minilessons, and activities to accompany

# Write Away

## WRITE SOURCE®

GREAT SOURCE EDUCATION GROUP
a Houghton Mifflin Company
Wilmington, Massachusetts

# A Few Words About the SourceBook

## Before you begin . . .

You need to know that this SourceBook should be used with the *Write Away* handbook. The SourceBook offers opportunities to practice the skills presented in the handbook. SourceBook activities include Practice Workshops, Minilessons, and MUG Shot Sentences.

## Practice Workshops

The Practice Workshops cover language skills and offer practice in writing and proofreading.

## Minilessons

Each Minilesson covers an important writing or learning idea from the handbook. Most Minilessons can be done on your own or with a partner.

## Daily MUG Shot Sentences

The MUG Shot Sentences review basic mechanics, usage, and grammar skills. Focused Sentences address one skill at a time. The Proofreading Sentences offer several different sentence problems for you to correct.

**Authors:** Pat Sebranek and Dave Kemper

Trademarks and trade names are shown in this book strictly for illustrative purposes and are the property of their respective owners. The authors' references herein should not be regarded as affecting their validity.

**Great Source** and **Write Source** are registered trademarks of Houghton Mifflin Company.

Printed in the United States of America

International Standard Book Number: 0-669-44046-9 (Pupil Edition)

   8 9 10 11 12 -POO- 02 01 00 99

International Standard Book Number: 0-669-44350-6 (Teacher Edition)

   4 5 6 7 8 9 10 11 12 -POO- 02 01 00 99

# Table of Contents

## Practice Workshops

### Using Punctuation

**3** Using Periods

**9** Using Question Marks

**11** Using Exclamation Points

**13** All About End Punctuation

**15** Using Commas

**25** Making Contractions

**27** Showing Ownership

**29** Using Quotation Marks

**33** Underlining Titles

### Checking Mechanics

**35** Using Capital Letters

**53** Reviewing Capitals

**55** Making Plurals

**63** Reviewing Plurals

**65** Using Abbreviations

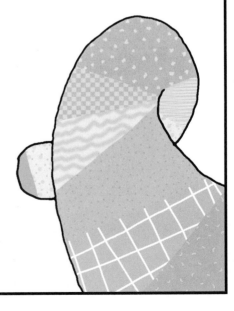

## Using the Right Word

**67** Using the Right Word 1
**69** Using the Right Word 2
**71** Using the Right Word 3
**73** Using the Right Word Review

## Checking Your Sentences

**75** Understanding Sentences
**77** Parts of a Sentence

## Understanding Our Language

**79** Using Nouns
**81** Singular and Plural Nouns
**83** Common and Proper Nouns
**85** More Common and Proper Nouns
**87** Pronouns
**89** More Pronouns
**91** Using Action Verbs
**93** More About Verbs
**95** Adjectives
**97** Using Articles

## Using Theme Words

**99** Using Theme Words

# Minilessons

## Using Punctuation

**103** Periods as End Punctuation

**103** Periods After Abbreviations

**104** Periods Between Dollars and Cents

**105** Question Marks

**105** Exclamation Points

**106** Commas in a Series

**106** Commas in Place Names

**107** Commas in Letters

**107** Commas and Quotation Marks

**108** Speakers' Words

**108** Punctuating Speakers' Words

**108** Quotation Marks for Titles

**109** Underlining Titles

**109** Commas

**110** Apostrophes in Contractions

**110** Apostrophes to Show Ownership

## Checking Mechanics

**111** Capital Letters

**114** Plurals Using "s"

**114** Plurals Using "es"

**115** Plurals That Change the Word

**115** Plurals: Words Ending in "y"

**116** Abbreviations

**116** Addresses

## Using the Right Word

**117** Using the Right Word

## Checking Your Sentences

**119** Adding Subjects or Verbs
**119** Complete Sentences
**120** Telling Sentences
**120** Asking Sentences
**120** Exclamatory Sentences

## Understanding Our Language

**121** Nouns
**121** Plural Nouns
**121** Proper Nouns
**122** Possessive Nouns
**122** Pronouns
**123** Verbs
**124** Past Tense Verbs
**124** Future Tense Verbs
**124** Irregular Verbs
**125** Adjectives

## Using Theme Words

**127** Days/Months
**127** Community Words
**128** Food Words
**128** Season/Weather Words

# MUG Shot Sentences

## Focused Sentences

**131** Periods
**134** Question Marks
**135** Exclamation Points
**136** Commas
**142** Apostrophes
**145** Quotation Marks
**146** Underlining
**147** Capital Letters
**154** Making Plurals
**155** Using the Right Word

## Proofreading Sentences

**159** Penguins
**160** Zebras
**161** Storms
**162** Tornadoes
**163** Seashore
**164** Frogs
**165** Caves
**166** Bridges
**167** Tunnels
**168** Mammals

# Practice Workshops

These activities use the basic language skills covered in the "Proofreader's Guide" of the *Write Away* handbook.

*Name* _____

# Using Periods as End Punctuation

A **period** is used as a signal to stop at the end of a sentence. You put a period at the end of a telling sentence.

**A** **Put periods at the end of these telling sentences.**

1. Our class lines up at the main door ____•___

2. Sometimes we make our teacher smile _____

3. We play indoors on rainy days _____

4. There are some great new books in the library _____

5. I like to write funny stories _____

**B** **Write two telling sentences about your school.**

1. _____

_____

2. _____

_____

**C** Put a period at the end of each sentence in this letter.

October 10, 1996

Dear Aunt Fran,

I like school this year There are 22 kids in my class A new boy sits next to me His name is Robert I think we're going to be friends I'll let you know in my next letter

Love,

Timmy

Now answer these questions about the letter.

1. How many telling sentences are in the letter? _____

2. How many periods are in the letter? _____

Name

# Using Periods After Abbreviations

Use a **period** after these abbreviations:

Mr.  Mrs.  Ms.  Dr.

Dr. Green    Mrs. Linn

(**Dr.** is the abbreviation for **doctor.**)

**A** **Put periods after the abbreviations in these sentences.**

1. Mrs. Linn is our teacher.

2. Mr and Mrs Linn have three rabbits.

3. Mr Linn gave the rabbits their names.

4. They are Ms Hop, Mr Skip, and Mrs Jump.

5. Mrs Linn took the rabbits to Dr Green for shots.

6. Dr Green said, "Those are good names!"

7. Mrs Linn told Dr Green that Mr Linn made up the names.

**B** Write two silly names for rabbits. One name should start with Mr. and one with Mrs. Then write two sentences that use the names.

Name _____

Name _____

1. _____

_____

_____

2. _____

_____

_____

**C** Write the names of four grown-ups. Be sure to write Mr., Mrs., Ms., or Dr. before each name.

1. _____

2. _____

3. _____

4. _____

*Name*
_____

# Using Periods Between Dollars and Cents

Use a **period** (decimal point) between dollars and cents.

$1.50     $3.00     $7.95

**A** Put periods (decimal points) between the dollars and cents in these sentences.

1. Dan made $4.3 5 selling lemonade and cookies.

2. I paid $1 0 0 for two cookies.

3. Dan put $1 3 5 in his bank.

4. He spent $3 0 0 for two movie tickets.

5. Tickets only cost $1 5 0 on Saturday afternoon.

6. My lunch ticket costs $2 7 5 this week.

7. Ms. Bank pays $3 5 0 for lunch.

8. I saved $8 0 0 for my new bike.

*Using Punctuation*     **7**

**B** **Fill in the blanks in the word problems below.**

1. $1.00 + $4.00 = _____

2. $8.00 − $2.00 = _____

3. $3.00 + $3.00 + $3.00 = _____

4. $5.00 − $2.00 = _____

5. $1.00 + $2.00 + $3.00 = _____

6. $4.00 + $1.00 + $1.00 = _____

**C** **Write each amount listed below in numerals.**

1. One dollar and fifty cents _____

2. One dollar and twenty cents _____

3. Five dollars and ten cents _____

4. Ten dollars and sixty-nine cents _____

5. Two dollars and no cents _____

6. Six dollars and fifty cents _____

*Name* _____

# Using Question Marks

Put a **question mark** after a sentence that asks a question.

What is the longest river in the world?

**A** Put a question mark after each sentence that asks a question. Put a period after all the other sentences.

1. The world's longest river is the Nile _____

2. Where is the Nile _____

3. The Nile River is in Africa _____

4. Are there crocodiles in the Nile _____

5. You could jump in and find out _____

6. Are you kidding _____

7. I'd rather just ask someone _____

8. Are you afraid of crocodiles _____

9. Who wouldn't be afraid _____

*Using Punctuation* **9**

**B** Put a period or a question mark at the end of each sentence in this paragraph.

Lots of animals live in rivers Of course, fish live in rivers What else lives in rivers Snails, frogs, and turtles live in rivers Have you heard of river otters They are very good at diving They can stay underwater for four minutes Do you know any other animals that dive

**C** Write two questions about rivers. Remember to use question marks!

1. _____

_____

2. _____

_____

*Name* _____

# Using Exclamation Points

Put an **exclamation point** after an "excited" word.

Help!        Yuck!

Also put an exclamation point after a sentence showing strong feelings.

Don't touch that!

**A** Put an exclamation point after each "excited" word and after each sentence that shows strong feelings.

1. I found a treasure map__!__

2. I don't believe you_____

3. It's true_____

4. Wow_____

5. Let's find the treasure_____

6. We'll be famous_____

7. This could be dangerous_____

8. I think I see a pirate_____

*Using Punctuation*   **11**

## B

**Some of these sentences need an exclamation point at the end. Some need a question mark. Put the correct end punctuation after each sentence.**

1. Look, Tom, it's a cave______
2. It's dark______
3. It's creepy______
4. Did you see that______
5. What is it______
6. It's a bat______
7. Wow, that's neat______
8. Here we go______

## C

**Imagine that you are in a dark cave. Write a sentence that ends with an exclamation point.**

______________________________________________

______________________________________________

______________________________________________

*Name* _____

# All About End Punctuation

Use a **period (.)** at the end of a telling sentence. Use a **question mark (?)** after a sentence that asks a question. Use an **exclamation point (!)** after a sentence that shows strong feelings.

 **Put the correct end punctuation after each sentence.**

1. Dad's taking us to the ice-cream store __!__

2. Hooray! Let's have a race to the car _____

3. What flavor will Dad choose _____

4. He likes hot fudge sundaes _____

5. What do you think Mom wants _____

6. She'll probably get frozen yogurt _____

7. What should we get _____

8. Let's get ice-cream sandwiches _____

*Using Punctuation*   **13**

**Write a telling sentence, a question, and a sentence showing strong feelings about your favorite dessert.**

Telling  Sentence: _____

_____

Question: _____

_____

Exclamatory  Sentence: _____

_____

**C**  **Interview a friend.  Write your friend's name, the question you asked, and your friend's answer.**

Friend's  Name: _____

Question: _____

_____

Answer: _____

_____

*Name* _____

# Using a Comma Between a City and a State

Put a **comma** between a city and a state.

Austin, Texas     Salem, Oregon

**A**  **Put commas between the cities and states below.**

1. Calumet **,** Michigan

2. Casper   Wyoming

3. Williamsburg   Virginia

4. Portland   Maine

5. Commerce   Texas

6. Dayton   Ohio

**B**  **Write the names of three cities and states shown on the United States map on page 305 in your handbook. Be sure to put a comma between the city and the state.**

1. _____

2. _____

3. _____

**Draw a picture of where you live. Beneath your drawing, write sentences about your picture. The first words have been written for you.**

I live in _____

_____

_____

_____

_____

*Name* _____

# Using a Comma Between the Day and the Year

December 1999

| S | M | T | W | T | F | S |
|---|---|---|---|---|---|---|
|   |   |   | 1 | 2 | 3 | 4 |
| 5 | 6 | 7 | 8 | 9 | 10 | 11 |
| (12) | 13 | 14 | 15 | 16 | 17 | 18 |
| 19 | 20 | 21 | 22 | 23 | 24 | ◇25◇ |
| 26 | 27 | 28 | 29 | 30 | 31 |   |

Put a **comma** between the day and the year.

January 17, 1999
November 12, 1999

**A** Look at the calendar on this page. Then write the correct month, day, and year.

1. Write the date that is circled.

   December 12, 1999

2. Write the date that has a diamond around it.

   _____

3. Write the date for the last day of the month.

   _____

**B** **Write the dates for the following days.  Be sure to include the month, day, and year.**

1. Your next birthday

_____

2. Today

_____

3. Tomorrow

_____

**C** **Write a true or make-believe story about the day you were born.  Include the date in your story.**

_____

_____

_____

_____

_____

Name _____

# Using Commas in Letters

Put **commas** after the greeting and the closing of a letter.

Dear Grandpa Joe, ← **greeting**
     I love my new fishing rod!  Thank you!
Can we go fishing soon?  I hope so!
       Love,
      Ben ↖ **closing**

 **A**  **Put commas where they belong in these letters.**

May 10, 1996
Dear Ben
    Ask your mom when your family is coming to Florida. Then we can go fishing.
     Love
     Grandpa Joe

May 18, 1996
Dear Grandpa Joe
    We are coming to see you on June 24 after school is out. I can't wait! My tackle box is ready.
     Love
     Ben

**B** Put commas in Grandpa's letter. Then pretend you are Ben. Write what you would say in your next letter to Grandpa Joe. Be sure to put commas in the right places.

May 24, 1996

Dear Ben

    I will be seeing you in one month! We'll camp out in a tent. We'll have a campfire.

        Love

        Grandpa Joe

_____
(Date)

_____
(Greeting)

_____

_____

_____

_____
(Closing)

_____
(Signature)

*Name* _____

# Using Commas Between Words in a Series

Put **commas** between words in a series.
The five senses are sight, hearing, taste, smell, and touch.

**A** **Put commas where they are needed in these sentences.**

1. Most foods taste sweet, sour, or salty.

2. Smell sight and taste help us enjoy food.

3. Almost everybody likes candy cookies and cake.

4. Pizza brownies and roses smell good.

5. Cats can see only black white and gray.

6. Dogs cats and bats hear all kinds of sounds.

7. Sounds can be loud soft or just right.

8. Teddy bears are soft cuddly and fuzzy.

*Using Punctuation* **21**

**List three or four things in each category below.**

| My favorite TASTES | My favorite SMELLS | My favorite SOUNDS |
|---|---|---|
| | | |
| | | |
| | | |
| | | |
| | | |

**C** Now write three sentences using some of the words in your lists. Remember to use commas between words in a series in your sentences.

1. _____

_____

2. _____

_____

3. _____

_____

*Name*
_____

# Using Commas to Set Off a Speaker's Words

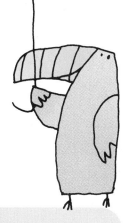

When you write a speaker's exact words, you may tell who is speaking at the **beginning** of the sentence, or at the **end** of the sentence.

Mr. Kent said, "Kari, you may begin your report."

"My report is on rain forests," Kari said.

 **Put commas where they are needed in these sentences.**

1. "Most rain forests are near the equator," Kari said.

2. Michael asked "What is it like in a rain forest?"

3. "Rain forests are warm, wet, and green all year " Kari answered.

4. She added "There can be rain more than 200 days a year."

5. "That's very interesting " said Mr. Kent.

*Using Punctuation*  **23**

**B** **Write what you think Bill and Regina might ask Kari about rain forests. Use quotation marks, question marks, and commas correctly.**

Bill asked _____

_____

_____

_____

_____

Regina asked _____

_____

_____

_____

**24**  *Using Punctuation*

*Name* _____

# Making Contractions

A **contraction** turns two words into one word. To make a contraction, you put an apostrophe where one or more letters are left out.

| Two Words | Contraction |
|-----------|-------------|
| does not  | doesn't     |
| he will   | he'll       |

 **In the first column, cross out the letters that are left out when the contraction is made.**

| Two Words | Contraction |
|-----------|-------------|
| 1. I am   | I'm         |
| 2. she will | she'll    |
| 3. he is  | he's        |
| 4. they are | they're   |
| 5. he would | he'd      |
| 6. has not | hasn't     |
| 7. we will | we'll      |
| 8. should not | shouldn't |

*Using Punctuation*   **25**

**B** **Make a contraction from each pair of words. Remember to use apostrophes!**

1. do  not  _____

2. that  is  _____

3. cannot  _____

4. I  have  _____

**C** **On each blank below, write the contraction for the words in parentheses.**

1. _____ going to make a mask.
   (I am)

2. _____ make it out of a paper bag.
   (I will)

3. _____ going to be a scary mask.
   (It is)

4. Dad _____ know I am making it.
   (does not)

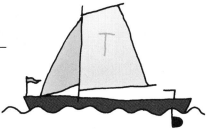

*Name*
_____

# Showing Ownership

Add an **apostrophe** and an "**s**" to a word to show ownership.

Tom has a boat.     It is Tom's boat.
The dog has a bone.     It is the dog's bone.

**A**  **Each phrase below shows ownership. Draw a picture in each box.**

| | |
|---|---|
| the cat's rug | the bird's nest |
| Susan's jump rope | my mother's hat |

*Using Punctuation*  **27**

**B** **Look at the picture on page 153 in your handbook. Then write words to show ownership in each blank. Remember to use an apostrophe and an "s."**

1. the_____ towel

2. the_____ sailboat

3. the_____ chair

4. the_____ pail

**C** **You can also show ownership by adding an apostrophe and an "s" to a name. Write the names below to show ownership.**

1. I see _____ purple pencil.
      (Marie)

2. This is _____ math book.
       (Don)

3. _____ backpack is heavier than mine.
      (Jane)

4. _____ idea notebook is on the desk.
      (Sol)

*Name* _____

# Using Quotation Marks Before and After a Speaker's Words

Comic strips make it easy to tell who is speaking. They use speech balloons. Here Mom and Steve are talking about dinner.

When you write sentences, you use **quotation marks** to show the speaker's exact words.

Steve asked, "Mom, can we make pizza for dinner?"

"That sounds really good to me," Mom said.

**A** Read the speech balloons. Then write the sentences below. Put quotation marks where they are needed.

Can we make pepperoni pizza?

Sure, but add a vegetable, too.

Steve asked, _____

_____

Mom answered, _____

_____

How about mushrooms?

Great choice!

Steve asked, _____

_____

Mom said, _____

_____

*Name* _____

# Using Quotation Marks for Titles

Put **quotation marks** around the titles of stories and poems.

**a story** — "Goldilocks"
**a poem** — "Monday Morning Good"

 **A** **Put quotation marks around the titles in these sentences.**

1. "The Tortoise and the Hare" is a fable.

2. The Ugly Duckling is my favorite fairy tale.

3. Eletelephony is a poem that makes me laugh.

4. I like the poem Beans, Beans, Beans.

5. We read the fable The Lion and the Mouse.

6. We read the poem Oodles of Noodles.

7. Did you read Rumpelstiltskin yet?

**B** Use your handbook to help you fill in each blank with the correct title.  Make sure to use quotation marks correctly.

1. The fable _____

   is on page 139.

2. You'll find a shape poem called _____

   on page 162.

3. An add-on story called _____

   is found on page 135.

4. _____ is the all-about-me story on

   page 77.

5. You'll find a poem called _____ on page 151.

**C** Write a sentence about a poem or a story you like.  Give the title and use quotation marks correctly.

_____

_____

_____

*Name* _____

# Underlining Titles

**Underline** the **titles** of books and magazines.

**a book** — We Were Tired of Living in a House

**a magazine** — 3, 2, 1 Contact

## A  Underline the titles in the following sentences.

1. My sister's favorite book is <u>Pocahontas</u>.

2. My grandmother has a book called <u>Mrs. Bird</u>.

3. <u>Kids Discover</u> is a magazine for kids.

4. The title of our handbook is <u>Write Away</u>.

5. <u>Ranger Rick</u> is a nature magazine for kids.

6. I just read <u>Ira Sleeps Over</u> by Bernard Waber.

7. My dad reads <u>National Geographic</u> every month.

8. Our teacher is reading <u>All About Sam</u> to us.

*Using Punctuation*  **33**

**B** **Complete the following sentences. Remember to underline the titles.**

1. My favorite book is _____

_____ .

2. My favorite magazine is _____

_____ .

3. The title of the last book I read was _____

_____ .

**C** **Draw a cover for one of your favorite books. Write the book title on your cover.**

*Name* _____

# Using Capital Letters to Begin Sentences

Always use a **capital letter** for the first word in a sentence.

We go to the park in the summer.

**A** Begin each of the following sentences with a capital letter.

O
1. ~~O~~ne day we had a picnic.

2. aunt Jill brought a big bowl of fruit salad.

3. grandma made lemonade and a chocolate cake.

4. we had sub sandwiches and taco chips.

5. all the kids played softball before lunch.

6. after the game everyone drank lemonade.

7. grandma's cake was the best part of the picnic.

8. the ants liked it, too.

*Checking Mechanics*  **35**

**B**  Put a capital letter at the beginning of each sentence.  Put a period at the end of each sentence.

there's a swimming pool at our park sometimes we go there for a swim i learned how to swim last year now I can go in the deep end of the pool my little sister can't swim yet she stays in the shallow end maybe I'll teach her how to swim

**C**  Write two sentences about things you like to do in the summer.  Remember to use capital letters and periods.

1. _____

_____

2. _____

_____

*Name* _____

# Using Capital Letters for Names and Titles

Use **capital letters** for people's names.

Christopher Robin

Use **capital letters** for titles that come before names.

Dr. Doolittle    Mrs. Piggle-Wiggle

 **Draw pictures of two people you know. Write their names below the pictures.**

*Checking Mechanics*    **37**

**B** Write an interesting sentence about each person you drew on page 37.

1. _____

_____

2. _____

_____

**C** Write sentences about three of your favorite grown-ups. Remember to use capital letters for their names and titles.

1. _____

_____

2. _____

_____

3. _____

_____

*Name* _____

# Using a Capital Letter for "I"

Use a **capital letter** for the word "I."

I have curly red hair.
I like to tap-dance.

 **A** **Write the word "I" in each of these sentences.**

1. Jimmy and ___I___ are friends.

2. Sometimes _____ go to his house.

3. _____ ride there on my bike.

4. Sometimes Jimmy and _____ play at the park.

 **B** **Write two sentences of your own using the word "I."**

1. _____

_____

2. _____

_____

*Checking Mechanics* **39**

**Draw a picture of yourself in the box below. Then write three sentences about yourself. Begin each sentence with the word "I."**

1. _____

_____

2. _____

_____

3. _____

_____

*Name* _____

# Using Capital Letters for Titles

Most words in titles begin with **capital letters.**

↘Tales of a Fourth Grade Nothing

Some words do not begin with capital letters (unless they are the first or last word of a title). Here are some examples:

a  an  the  and  but  of  to  with  by  for

 **A** **Write the four underlined book titles correctly on the lines below.**

I went to the library yesterday. I found some wonderful books! I checked out <u>my great-aunt arizona</u>, <u>boxcar children</u>, <u>the three sillies</u>, and <u>the new kid on the block</u>.

1. <u>My Great-Aunt Arizona</u>

2. _____

3. _____

4. _____

**B** Interview yourself! Write down the titles of your favorite book and magazine.

Book: _____

Magazine: _____

**C** Write a note telling someone about your favorite book.

Dear_____,












Your friend,

_____

*Name* _____

# Using Capital Letters for Days of the Week

Use **capital letters** for days of the week.

**S**unday     **W**ednesday

**A** **Answer these questions.  Remember to use capital letters correctly.**

1. Which day comes after Saturday? _____ Sunday _____

2. Which day is between Tuesday and Thursday?

   _____

3. Which day begins with the letter "F"? _____

4. Which day is the first day of the school week?

   _____

5. Which day is your least favorite day? _____

6. Which day is your favorite day? _____

7. Which day comes before Friday? _____

*Checking Mechanics*  **43**

**B** Put the days of the week in the correct order starting with Sunday.

Thursday     Sunday     Tuesday     Monday

Friday     Wednesday     Saturday

1. _____

2. _____

3. _____

4. _____

5. _____

6. _____

7. _____

Draw a picture about your favorite day of the week.

Name _____

# Using Capital Letters for Months of the Year

Use **capital letters** for the months of the year.

February    May

**A** **Use capital letters for the months in these sentences.**

1. The first day of spring is in ~~m~~March.

2. The first day of summer is in june.

3. The first day of fall is in september.

4. The first day of winter is in december.

5. The first month of the year is january.

6. The shortest month is february.

7. Usually july and august are the hottest months.

8. april showers bring spring flowers.

## B Here are three more months. Write each month correctly.

may      _____

october    _____

november   _____

## C Write one sentence about each month above.

1. _____

_____

_____

2. _____

_____

_____

3. _____

_____

_____

Name

# More Practice with Capital Letters

Use **capital letters** for the months of the year.

 **A** **Read the sentences below. Write the month correctly on the line after each sentence.**

1. Labor Day is in september. _September_

2. Groundhog Day is in february. _____

3. Handwriting Day is the 12th of january. _____

4. Arbor Day is in april. _____

5. Thanksgiving Day is in november. _____

6. Halfway Day is on the second of july. _____

7. My birthday is in june. _____

8. Memorial Day is the last Monday in may. _____

9. Fire Prevention Week is during october. _____

*Checking Mechanics*  **47**

**B** **Unscramble these months and write them correctly on the lines below. Remember to use a capital letter for the first letter!**

1. uejn _____

2. gsatuu _____

3. hamrc _____

4. yrjnuaa _____

5. larip _____

6. yma _____

7. tbreoco _____

8. eeedmbcr _____

9. eyfbarru _____

10. ljuy _____

11. ervbnome _____

12. tpbreesme _____

*Name* _____

# Using Capital Letters for Holidays

Use **capital letters** for the names of holidays.

F̶ather's D̶ay    T̶hanksgiving D̶ay

**A**  **Use capital letters for the holidays in these sentences.**

N  Y  D
1. N̶ew Y̶ear's D̶ay is in January.

2. We made cards for valentine's day.

3. mother's day is always in May.

4. Two holidays in June are father's day and flag day.

5. July 4 is independence day.

6. The first Monday in September is labor day.

7. In February we celebrate presidents' day.

8. Christmas day is on December 25.

*Checking Mechanics*  **49**

**B** Write the names of three holidays that were not found in the sentences you just marked.

1. _____

2. _____

3. _____

**C** Now use the names of those three holidays in sentences.

1. _____

_____

_____

2. _____

_____

_____

3. _____

_____

*Name* _____

# Using Capital Letters for Names of Places

Use **capital letters** for the names of places.

| **City** | **State** | **Country** |
|----------|-----------|-------------|
| Carson City | Nevada | France |
| Rome | Iowa | Chad |

 **A** **Write the city, state, or country correctly in the following sentences.**

1. Make Way for Ducklings takes place in the city of boston. _____Boston_____

2. Disney World is in florida. _____

3. My grandma is from ireland. _____

4. Mt. Fuji is in japan. _____

5. The Bulls are a chicago team. _____

6. The Peach State is georgia. _____

7. The capital of Alaska is juneau. _____

*Checking Mechanics*  **51**

1. Which two states have "South" in their names?

   _____

   _____

2. Which two states begin with the letter "K"?

   _____

   _____

3. Which three states have only four letters in their names?

   _____

   _____

   _____

4. Which state do you live in?

   _____

5. Name a state that is near your home state.

   _____

6. Which state has four eyes (i's) but cannot see?

   _____

*Name*

# Reviewing Capitals

This activity reviews some of the different ways to use **capital letters**.

**A** Put capital letters where they are needed. (There are 19 in all.) Watch for these things:

* ✳ first word in a sentence
* ✳ names and titles of people
* ✳ names of places

O̶ur class is studying rivers.  mr. banks read a book to us about the nashau river.  the book was written by lynne cherry.  we also learned about the nile river in africa.  it is the longest river in the world.  ms. johnson visited our class.  she went down the amazon river on a raft!  she showed slides of her trip.

*Checking Mechanics*   **53**

**B** **Put capital letters where they are needed. (There are 11 in all.) Watch for these things:**
  * a speaker's first word
  * names of days and months
  * names of holidays

1. Ed said, "my favorite day is sunday.   What's yours?"

2. "sunday is my favorite day, too," I answered.

3. "what's your favorite month?" Joan asked.

4. I said, "my favorite month is july, because it's summer, and that's when I was born."

5. Joan said, "my favorite month is december, because that's when we celebrate hanukkah."

6. "that's when we celebrate christmas," I said.

**C** **Put capital letters where they are needed in these titles.**

1. the lion king

2. beauty and the beast

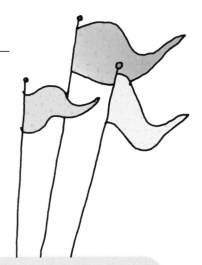

*Name* _____

# Making Plurals

**Plural** means more than one. For most nouns, you make the plural by adding an "**s**."

desk  desk**s**       window   window**s**

**A**  Here is a list of things that may be in your classroom. Write the plural forms of the nouns. Then add two of your own examples.

1. flag          _____ flags _____

2. table         _____

3. eraser        _____

4. pencil        _____

5. book          _____

6. marker        _____

7. door          _____

8. ruler         _____

9. _____    _____

10. _____   _____

*Checking Mechanics*

## B

**Fill in the blanks by changing the singular word under the line into a plural word.**

There are 16 ______________ (girl) and 10 ______________ (boy) in my class this year. We have one teacher and two ______________ (helper). There are three learning ______________ (center) in the classroom. In the reading center there are lots of ______________ (magazine). The art center has some very bright ______________ (marker). In the writing center there's a whole box of ______________ (pencil) and many different ______________ (kind) of paper. I love my classroom!

**Write a sentence telling how many boys and girls there are in your class.**

______________________________________________

______________________________________________

______________________________________________


© Great Source. All rights reserved.

*Name* _____

# Making Plurals Using "s" and "es"

For most nouns, you make the **plurals** by adding an "**s**."

| | |
|---|---|
| one bird | two bird**s** |
| a bike | four bike**s** |

For some nouns, you need to do more. You add "**es**" to words that end in **sh, ch, s, x,** or **z.**

| | |
|---|---|
| a bush | some bush**es** |
| a box | two box**es** |

**A** Write the plurals of the following nouns. It's easy—just add an "s."

1. bug    _____bugs_____

2. river _____

3. eye _____

4. ear _____

5. apple _____

6. dog _____

7. house _____

8. desk _____

9. tree _____

10. lake _____

**B** Make the following nouns plural. They all end in *sh*, *ch*, *s*, *x*, or *z*. That means you need to add "es."

1.  brush _____

2.  lunch _____

3.  class _____

4.  fox _____

5.  buzz _____

6.  boss _____

7.  bunch _____

8.  dish _____

**C** Fill in each blank with the correct plural. You will need to add an "s" to some nouns, and "es" to other nouns.

1.  At the petting zoo there are baby _____
    (lion)

    and _____ .
        (fox)

2.  There are three _____ and
                    (hamster)

    two _____ in my classroom.
            (gerbil)

3.  My mom makes _____ for me and
                    (lunch)

    my two _____ .
                (brother)

*Name* _____

# Making Plurals by Changing Words

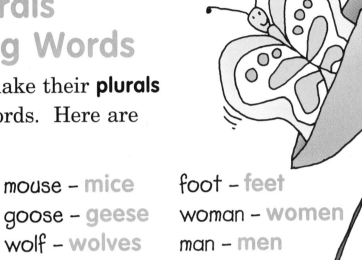

A few nouns make their **plurals** by changing the words. Here are some examples:

child – children    mouse – mice    foot – feet
wife – wives    goose – geese    woman – women
knife – knives    wolf – wolves    man – men

 **A**  **Fill in each blank with the correct plural from the nouns above.**

1. There's a song about three blind _____mice_____ .

2. You clap with your hands and walk with your _____ .

3. Set the table with _____, forks, and spoons.

4. Ducks and _____ like to swim in ponds.

5. Sheep need to be protected from _____ .

6. Cartoons are for _____, but_____

   and _____ watch them, too.

7. Husbands have _____ .

**B** Write the plural of each noun. Try to complete the list without looking back.

1. foot _____     6. wolf _____

2. knife _____     7. goose _____

3. mouse _____     8. wife _____

4. child _____     9. woman _____

5. man _____

Draw a picture about one of the sentences on page 59.

*Name* _____

# Making Plurals of Words That End in "y"

Here are two rules for making **plurals** of nouns ending in "**y**":

**Rule 1**  If there is a vowel right before the "**y**," just add "**s**."

turkey    turkeys

**Rule 2**  If there is a consonant right before the "**y**," change the "**y**" to "**i**" and add "**es**."

puppy        puppies

**A**  **Make the following nouns plural using Rule 1 or Rule 2.**

1. story        _____ stories _____

2. candy        _____

3. donkey      _____

4. key          _____

5. baby         _____

6. day          _____

*Checking Mechanics*    **61**

Here are some more nouns that end in "y." Write their plurals. Be sure to check the letter before the "y."

1. monkey _____     5. kitty _____

2. lady _____     6. battery _____

3. fly _____     7. holiday _____

4. toy _____     8. bay _____

Pick three of the plurals you just made. Use each one in a sentence.

1. _____

_____

2. _____

_____

3. _____

_____

*Name* _____

# Reviewing Plurals

This activity reviews making **plurals**.

**A** **Make the plurals of these nouns by adding "s" or "es."**

1. glass ____glasses____

2. brush _____

3. frog _____

4. lunch _____

5. bus _____

6. hand _____

7. dress _____

8. worm _____

**B** **Write the plural of each of these words. Just add "s" or change "y" to "i" and add "es."**

1. monkey _____

2. puppy _____

3. day _____

4. story _____

5. turkey _____

6. toy _____

**C** **Write the plurals of these nouns. Remember, some words change to make the plural.**

1. mouse _____      4. woman _____

2. foot    _____      5. knife    _____

3. child   _____      6. man     _____

**Draw a funny picture about feet.**

*Name* _____

# Using Abbreviations

Put a **period** after titles of people:
**Mr.  Mrs.  Ms.  Dr.**

Ms. Walters        Mr. Johnson

 **A** **Put periods after the abbreviations in these sentences.**

1. Mr. Forest is our next-door neighbor.

2. Mr and Mrs Forest have a very big garden.

3. Mrs Forest works in her garden on cool mornings.

4. Her friend Dr Maynard stops to visit before work.

5. Mrs Forest gives Dr Maynard some pretty

   flowers to take to the office.

6. After dinner, Mr Forest likes to weed the garden.

7. Mrs Forest helps him water the plants.

*Checking Mechanics*    **65**

**B** Think of four people who work in your school. Write their names below. Be sure to write Mr., Mrs., Ms., Miss, or Dr. before each.

1. _____

2. _____

3. _____

4. _____


**C** Choose two of the people. Write a sentence about each person.

1. _____

_____

2. _____

_____

*Name* _____

# Using the Right Word 1

Some words sound alike, but they have different spellings. They also have different meanings. (These words are **homophones**.) Here are some examples:

I *hear* you.      I am *here*.

 **Fill in each blank with "here" or "hear."**

1. I asked my dog Dan to come _____ here _____ .

2. Can you _____ what I am saying?

3. Did you _____ what happened to Sara?

4. _____ is the ball I thought I lost.

5. I _____ music.

6. Dan can _____ better than people.

**B** **Write a sentence using "hear" and "here."**

_____

_____

*Using the Right Word*  **67**

**C** Read the example sentences using "no" and "know." Then fill in each blank with the correct word.

Susan said, "**No** thanks."
I **know** about computers.

1. There is _____ more ice cream.

2. I _____ where to get some.

3. Just answer yes or _____ .

4. Do you _____ the new girl?

5. I don't _____ her yet.

6. There is _____ school tomorrow.

**D** Write a sentence using "no" and "know."

_____

_____

*Name* _____

# Using the Right Word 2

Some words sound alike, but they have different spellings. They also have different meanings. (These words are **homophones**.) Here are some examples:

These shoes are new.    I knew the answer.

 **A**    **Fill in each blank with "new" or "knew."**

1. I got a _____new_____ raincoat.

2. My mom _____ it was going to rain today.

3. My sister got _____ boots.

4. Dave wrote a _____ story.

5. Mike said he _____ how it would end.

6. We start a _____ chapter today.

 **B**    **Write a sentence using "new" and "knew."**

_____

_____

*Using the Right Word*

**C** **Read the example sentences using "their," "there," and "they're." Then fill in each blank with the correct word.**

We saw **their** new puppy.
("Their" shows ownership.)

**There** are three pets now.

**They're** lots of fun.
(They're = they are.)

1. _____ are four kids in the Clark family.

2. We play freeze tag in _____ backyard.

3. _____ my next-door neighbors.

4. _____ mother loves animals.

5. Sometimes _____ busy feeding the pets.

6. _____ are messes to clean up, too!

**D** **Write a funny sentence using two of these words: "their," "there," and "they're."**

_____

_____

*Name* _____

# Using the Right Word 3

Some words sound alike, but they have different spellings. They also have different meanings. (These words are **homophones**.) Here are some examples:

I have two cats.   I have a dog, too.   I go to Pine Elementary.

**A** **Fill in each blank with "two," "to," or "too." "Too" can mean "also" or "more than enough."**

1. We are going _____to_____ the beach.

2. We can only stay for _____ hours.

3. Can I come, _____ ?

4. I like to take a radio _____ the beach.

5. Just don't play it _____ loud.

**B** **Write a sentence using "two," "to," and "too."**

_____

_____

*Using the Right Word*

**C** Read the example sentences using "read" and "red." Then fill in each blank with the correct word.

I **read** that book.     My notebook is **red**.

1. The U.S. flag is _____ , white, and blue.

2. Our class _____ about the flag.

3. Candy canes are _____ and white.

4. Our teacher uses a _____ pen.

5. Casey _____ his story to the class.

6. Tina _____ a poem.

**D** Write a sentence using "read" and "red."

_____

_____

*Name* _____

# Using the Right Word Review

This activity reviews the **homophones** you have practiced.

 **A** **Write the correct word in each blank.**

1. Sam took _____**two**_____ rats _____ school.
                (two, to, too)               (two, to, too)

2. The white rat had _____ eyes.
                 (read, red)

3. Someone yelled, "Don't bring them in _____ !"
                 (hear, here)

4. Miss Green said, "I _____ what to do."
                 (no, know)

5. The rats like to sleep in _____ .
                 (hear, here)

6. I _____ Sam likes his rats.
       (no, know)

7. He has a pet spider, _____ .
             (two, to, too)

               *Using the Right Word*   **73**

8. Don has a _____ pet parrot.
   (new, knew)

9. _____ are more than 300 kinds of parrots.
   (Their, There, They're)

10. First he _____ all about parrots.
    (read, red)

11. Then he _____ how to take care of one.
    (new, knew)

12. You should _____ the parrot talk!
    (hear, here)

**B** Write one sentence for each of these words: "to," "two," "too."

1. _____

   _____

2. _____

   _____

3. _____

   _____

Name _____

# Understanding Sentences

A **sentence** tells a complete thought.

This is not a complete thought:
### On the window.

This is a complete thought:
### There is a bug on the window.

 **A**　**Check whether the group of words is a complete thought or not.**

|  | Complete Thought | |
|---|---|---|
|  | **Yes** | **No** |
| 1. From the downstairs music room. | _____ | ✓ |
| 2. The sound was very loud. | _____ | _____ |
| 3. Covered his ears. | _____ | _____ |
| 4. After that. | _____ | _____ |
| 5. He shut the front door. | _____ | _____ |
| 6. Max played the drums. | _____ | _____ |
| 7. Sue played the piano. | _____ | _____ |
| 8. Mom the silver flute. | _____ | _____ |

**B** **Fill in each blank with a word that completes the thought.**

1. _____ was playing with a ball.

2. The _____ rolled down the hill.

3. _____ ran after it.

4. Then a big, hairy _____ ran after it, too.

5. The _____ got the ball and kept running.

6. Was the _____ gone for good?

**Draw a picture about sentence 4.**

Name _____

# Parts of a Sentence

Every **sentence** has two parts, the **subject** and the **verb**.

$\underline{\text{Joe}}$ $\underline{\underline{\text{planted}}}$ a seed.

**subject** ↗        ↖ **verb**

The subject is the naming part.  The verb tells what the subject is doing.

 **A** **Underline the subject with one line and the verb with two lines.**

1. $\underline{\text{Joe}}$ $\underline{\underline{\text{watered}}}$ his seed every day.

2. He waited for it to grow.

3. A tiny leaf popped out.

4. The leaf grew larger.

5. A flower bloomed one morning.

6. Joe ran to tell his mom.

7. Mom smiled at Joe.

8. Joe gave the flower to his Mom.

*Checking Your Sentences*  **77**

## B  Write a verb for each sentence.

1. Mom _____ cookies.

2. I _____ her.

3. I _____ the eggs.

4. I _____ the bowls.

5. Mom _____ the cookies in the oven.

6. I always _____ the first cookie.

## C  Check whether the underlined word is a subject or a verb.

|  | Subject | Verb |
|---|---|---|
| 1. Your body <u>has</u> a lot of bones. | _____ | _____ |
| 2. Your longest <u>bone</u> is in your leg. | _____ | _____ |
| 3. Your ribs <u>look</u> like a cage. | _____ | _____ |
| 4. Your smallest <u>bone</u> is in your ear. | _____ | _____ |
| 5. <u>Jellyfish</u> have no bones. | _____ | _____ |
| 6. A <u>skeleton</u> is all bones. | _____ | _____ |

**78**  *Checking Your Sentences*

*Name* _____

# Using Nouns

A **noun** names a person, a place, or a thing.

| Person | Place | Thing |
|--------|-------|-------|
| student | house | cake |
| friend | mall | fishing pole |

 **Write what each word is: "person," "place," or "thing." Add two nouns of your own.**

1. policeman   _____person_____

2. library   _____

3. hammer   _____

4. teacher   _____

5. pencil   _____

6. store   _____

7. _____   _____

8. _____   _____

*Understanding Our Language*   **79**

**B** Write **N** if the word is a noun. Write **X** if the word is not a noun. Add two words of your own.

_____ 1. paper      _____ 4. bring      _____ 7. and

_____ 2. go         _____ 5. girl       _____ 8. _____

_____ 3. bee        _____ 6. store      _____ 9. _____

**C** Underline the noun in each sentence.

1. The bus is yellow.

2. The spider jumped.

3. This game is hard.

4. Look at the duck!

5. The sky looks pretty.

6. A friend called.

Write a sentence about your favorite place. Then underline the nouns in your sentence.

_____

_____

_____

*Name* _____

# Singular and Plural Nouns

**Singular** means one.

elephant

**Plural** means more than one.

elephants

Plural nouns usually end with "**s**."

**A** **Write S if the word is singular. Write P if the word is plural.**

__P__ 1. boxes          _____ 4. rug

_____ 2. table          _____ 5. truck

_____ 3. chairs         _____ 6. toys

**B** **Write S if the underlined word is singular. Write P if the underlined word is plural.**

_____ 1. I like art.          _____ 3. Paints are messy.

_____ 2. I have crayons.      _____ 4. It's for my sister.

*Understanding Our Language*   **81**

## C    Underline the plural noun in each sentence.

1. The cow has black and white spots.

2. Some piglets are pink.

3. Potatoes spilled out of the grocery bag.

4. My sister baked chocolate chip cookies yesterday.

5. Tony took off his muddy shoes.

6. Erin held the tiny kittens.

 **Draw a picture about one of the sentences above.**

*Name* _____

# Common and Proper Nouns

A **common noun** tells what a thing is.
A **proper noun** tells a thing's name.

| Common Noun | Proper Noun |
|---|---|
| boy | Tony Prada |
| school | Hill Elementary |
| city | Lexington |

A proper noun begins with a capital letter.
Sometimes it can be more than one word.

 **A**    **Underline the common noun in each sentence.**

1. The <u>class</u> is busy writing.

2. The teacher likes to help.

3. The girl is reading quietly.

4. The street is shiny and wet.

5. The sandy beach is hot.

6. Let's swim in the pool!

7. My puppy is furry and brown.

8. He has a red collar.

## B   Underline the proper noun in each sentence.

1. We stopped at Jefferson Library.

2. Susie wanted a book about horses.

3. This book is about President Lincoln.

4. Principal Brown visited the library.

5. He speaks Spanish.

6. Rosa Perez does, too.

## C   Write C if the underlined word is a common noun. Write P if the underlined word is a proper noun.

_____ 1. My neighbor walks her <u>dog</u> each afternoon.

_____ 2. My neighbor's name is <u>Mrs. Lee</u>.

_____ 3. Her <u>dog</u> likes me.

_____ 4. <u>Alf</u> is a funny dog.

_____ 5. One day he got on a <u>bus</u>.

_____ 6. The bus <u>driver</u> said, "No dogs on the bus!"

*Name*

# More Common and Proper Nouns

A **common noun** tells what a thing is.
A **proper noun** tells a thing's name.

| Common Noun | Proper Noun |
|---|---|
| holiday | New Year's Day |
| country | Mexico |

A proper noun begins with a capital letter. Sometimes it can be more than one word.

**A**  **Write C if the word is a common noun. Write P if the word is a proper noun.**

__C__ 1. cat

_____ 2. Disneyland

_____ 3. library

_____ 4. Washington, D.C.

_____ 5. flag

_____ 6. Jennifer

_____ 7. Main Street

_____ 8. book

_____ 9. mountain

_____ 10. Rocky Mountains

**B** **Draw a line from each common noun to the proper noun that fits with it.**

1. girl                    U.S.A.

2. boy                     Fluffy

3. cat                     "The Three Bears"

4. country                 Tom

5. story                   Lisa

**C** **Write C if the underlined word is a common noun. Write P if the underlined word is a proper noun.**

_____ 1. Today is <u>Christmas</u>!

_____ 2. There is no <u>school</u> today.

_____ 3. The <u>air</u> is freezing cold.

_____ 4. <u>Aunt Lizzie</u> visited us.

_____ 5. Kevin brought ribbon <u>candy</u>.

_____ 6. He is from <u>Korea</u>.

*Name* _____

# Pronouns

A **pronoun** is a word that takes the place of a noun.

| **Noun** | **Pronoun** |
|---|---|
| Sandy left. | I left. |
| Sandy and Ray left. | We left. |
| Todd did it. | He did it. |
| Sally laughed. | She laughed. |
| The rope broke. | It broke. |
| The skates are too big. | They are too big. |

 **A** **Circle the pronouns that replace the underlined nouns in the sentences below.**

1. Holly gave Katy a Mexican coin.

   (She) gave Katy a Mexican coin.

2. Katy put the coin in a safe place.

   Katy put it in a safe place.

3. Peggy and Jo wanted to see the coin.

   They wanted to see the coin.

4. Then Jay asked to see it, too.

   Then he asked to see it, too.

*Understanding Our Language* **87**

**B** **Draw a line from each noun to the pronoun that could replace it.**

1. Dad and Mom                    he

2. the girl                       it

3. Jay                            I

4. the TV                         we

5. Shari and I                    they

6. _____      she
   (write your name here)

**C** **In each sentence, write a pronoun to replace the noun. If you need help, check the list of pronouns on page 278 in your handbook.**

1. _____ went to a movie.
   (Jim and Ray)

2. _____ broke his arm.
   (The boy)

3. A doctor fixed _____ .
   (the arm)

4. _____ is a good writer.
   (Jane)

*Name* _____

# More Pronouns

A **pronoun** can take the place of a possessive noun. A possessive noun shows ownership.

| **Noun** | **Pronoun** |
|---|---|
| Jim's computer | my computer |
| Jim and Sam's kite | our kite |
| Jan's bicycle | her bicycle |
| Dave's skateboard | his skateboard |
| the bird's wing | its wing |
| Mike and Laura's poem | their poem |

 **Circle the pronouns that replace the underlined nouns in the sentences below.**

1. <u>Juanita's</u> coat is hanging up.

   (Her) coat is hanging up.

2. At the picnic, <u>Jake's</u> lunch fell into the water.

   At the picnic, his lunch fell into the water.

3. Yesterday <u>Sam and Sarah's</u> bus left early.

   Yesterday their bus left early.

**B** **Underline the pronoun in each sentence. Draw a picture about one of the sentences.**

1. Here is my pet rat.

2. Dad likes its pink ears.

3. Mom likes its long tail.

4. Bogart is our favorite pet.

5. He has red eyes.

6. Ted pets his white fur.

7. We bought a blue cage.

**C** **Draw a line to the pronoun that can replace the underlined words.**

1. I heard Tim and Judy's song.        ours

2. I know your sister's name.          Its

3. Here comes Ricky's friend.          their

4. The book's cover got wet.           his

5. The treehouse is yours and mine.    her

*Name* _____

# Using Action Verbs

There are different kinds of **verbs**.
Some verbs show action:

Mom found our jump rope.
She gave it to us.

**A** **Underline the action verb in each sentence.**

1. Al <u>brings</u> the rope.

2. Eli and Linda hold the rope.

3. Linda starts the rope twirling.

4. The other kids count for Al.

5. Scott's dog Stripe barks at Al.

6. Sometimes Al jumps 100 times!

7. Then Linda takes a turn.

8. Mother waves from the window.

9. She points at Stripe.

10. The kids laugh.

*Understanding Our Language* **91**

**B** **Here are some more action verbs. Fill in each blank with a verb from this box.**

| | | |
|---|---|---|
| dive | growl | laugh |
| roars | visit | eat |

1. Paul and Ann _____ the zoo.

2. They _____ at some lions.

3. One of the lions _____ back.

4. The elephants _____ lots of peanuts.

5. The polar bears _____ into the pool.

6. Paul and Ann _____ at the prairie dogs.

**Draw a zoo picture.**

Name _____

# More About Verbs

**Action verbs** show action.  Here are some examples:

kick    tell    throw    ask    run    write

**Linking verbs** complete a thought or an idea.  Here are some examples:

am    was    is    were    are    be

**A**    **Write A if the underlined verb is an action verb.  Write L if the verb is a linking verb.**

_A_ 1. Soccer players <u>kick</u> the ball.

____ 2. Football players <u>throw</u> the ball.

____ 3. I <u>am</u> cold.

____ 4. Pat and Rob <u>run</u> around the track.

____ 5. She <u>is</u> a fast runner.

____ 6. They <u>are</u> both in second grade.

____ 7. He <u>paints</u> pictures.

____ 8. Pete and Joni <u>were</u> sick.

*Understanding Our Language*    **93**

**B**

Pick three action verbs from the list on page 281 in your handbook. Use each action verb in a sentence.

1. _____

_____

2. _____

_____

3. _____

_____

**C**

Now pick two linking verbs from the previous page and use them in sentences.

1. _____

_____

2. _____

_____

*Name* _____

# Adjectives

An **adjective** describes a noun or a pronoun. An adjective often comes before the word it describes.

Megan has long hair.
Randy wears a black cap.

Sometimes an **adjective** comes after the word it describes.

They are hungry.

**A** Underline the adjective that describes each circled noun.

1. Elephants are <u>huge</u> (animals.)

2. They have wrinkled (skin.)

3. Their ivory (tusks) are long (teeth.)

4. Elephants use their floppy (ears) as giant (fans.)

5. An elephant's trunk works as a useful (tool.)

6. It can pick up small (peanuts.)

7. A cool (river) is an elephant's favorite (place)

*Understanding Our Language*  **95**

**B** Fill in each blank with an adjective that describes the underlined noun.

1. Elephants make _____ <u>noises</u>.

2. Elephants have _____ <u>trunks</u>.

3. They have _____ <u>feet</u>.

4. Elephants can carry _____ <u>loads</u>.

5. Would you take a _____ <u>ride</u> on an

   elephant?

6. How would you get on a _____ <u>elephant</u>?

**C** In these sentences, each adjective describes the circled pronoun. Underline the adjectives.

1. (You) are smart.          5. (It) is green.

2. (He) is funny.            6. (We) are cold.

3. (They) look tired.        7. (She) feels sick.

4. (I) am hungry.            8. (They) taste stale.

*Name* _____

# Using Articles

The words "**a**," "**an**," and "**the**" are called **articles**.

Use "**a**" before a consonant sound.

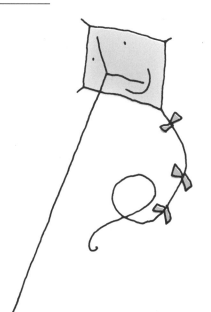

↗**a** kite

Use "**an**" before a vowel sound.

↗**an** ocean

**A**    **Write "a" or "an" before the following words.**

_____**an**_____ 1. attic      _____ 10. whale

_____ 2. chicken      _____ 11. shadow

_____ 3. shovel      _____ 12. envelope

_____ 4. elephant      _____ 13. idea

_____ 5. tooth      _____ 14. monkey

_____ 6. giant      _____ 15. orange

_____ 7. dinosaur      _____ 16. package

_____ 8. apple      _____ 17. kettle

_____ 9. spider      _____ 18. inchworm

     *Understanding Our Language*    **97**

**B** Fill in the word "a" or "an" in the spaces below.

One day _____ spider with yellow feet climbed

to the top of _____ slide. The slide was in _____

park. Soon the spider heard _____ radio playing her

favorite song. The song was _____ old tune called

"The Eensy Weensy Spider." The spider began to tap her

eight yellow feet. _____ inchworm heard the music,

too. He inched his way over to the slide and began to tap

all of his feet. What _____ funny sight to see.

_____ spider and _____ inchworm were dancing in

the park!

**Draw a picture of the spider and the inchworm.**

*Name*
_____

# Using Theme Words

Lists of **theme words** can help you choose and spell interesting words for your writing.

 **A** **Think of a favorite topic. Then list your own theme words below.**

Topic: _____

<table>
<tr><td></td><td></td></tr>
<tr><td></td><td></td></tr>
<tr><td></td><td></td></tr>
<tr><td></td><td></td></tr>
<tr><td></td><td></td></tr>
<tr><td></td><td></td></tr>
</table>

**B** **Write three sentences that use one or more of your theme words.**

1. _____

_____

2. _____

_____

3. _____

_____

**Make a picture about one theme word that names something.**

# Minilessons

The minilessons address skills covered in the "Proofreader's Guide" of the handbook. They offer practice in everything from punctuation to writing sentences to history facts.

# Using Punctuation Minilessons

Worms are wiggly.  . . . . . **Periods as End Punctuation**

**WRITE** three telling sentences about worms.  **USE** the correct end punctuation.

Dr. for Doctor . . . . . . . . . **Periods After Abbreviations**

Mr., Mrs., Ms., and Dr. are abbreviations.  They are used before people's names.

*Example:* Mrs. Brown

**WRITE** your teacher's name with the correct abbreviation before it.  Then **WRITE** the names of two other grown-ups you know.

Ms. Pinky Pig . . . . . . . . . . **Periods After Abbreviations**

**PRETEND** that you are going to write a fable about a family of pigs.  **MAKE UP** names for four pigs.  **USE** Mr., Mrs., Ms., or Dr. before each name.

## Think of a number. . . . . . . **Periods Between Dollars and Cents**

**ASK** a partner to pick an amount of money that is between one dollar and ten dollars. It should have both dollars and cents. **WRITE** the amount in numerals. **USE** a dollar sign, and put a period between dollars and cents.

*Example:* If your partner says, "Two dollars and ten cents," you write $2.10.

## How much? . . . . . . **Periods Between Dollars and Cents**

**FIND** the prices on things you see in a catalog or a grocery flier. **MAKE** a chart showing the name of each thing and its price. Make sure to **USE** dollar signs and periods. Your chart should have at least five things. Here's an example to get you started.

| Item | Price |
|---|---|
| corn chips | $1.29 |

## How do you end a question? . . . . . . . . . . . . . . . . **Question Marks**

**COMPLETE** each question below.  Make sure to use the correct end punctuation. The first one has been done for you.

1. **Who** _____ spilled paint on the floor? _____

2. **What** _____

3. **When** _____

4. **Where** _____

5. **Why** _____

6. **How** _____

## Wow! . . . . . . . . . . . . . . . . . . . . . . . **Exclamation Points**

An exclamation point is used after an "excited" word.
**WRITE** each word below as an "excited" word by using the correct punctuation.  On another piece of paper, draw a picture to go with one of the "excited" words.

1. **Ouch** _____     4. **Jump** _____

2. **Stop** _____     5. **Wow**_____

3. **Snakes**_____     6. **Run**_____

*Using Punctuation Minilessons*  **105**

## I got lost at the mall! . . . . . . . . . **Exclamation Points**

An exclamation point is used after a sentence that shows strong feelings. **WRITE** two or three sentences about a time when you were excited, or happy, or scared. **USE** an exclamation point after at least one of your sentences.

## Rain, Snow, Wind, and Hail . . . . **Commas in a Series**

**USE** commas correctly as you follow these directions. **WRITE** a sentence that lists four funny things. **WRITE** a sentence that lists four things you learn about in school. **WRITE** a sentence that lists three holidays. **LOOK** at page 251 in your handbook if you need help.

## I flew to Cleveland, Ohio. . . **Commas in Place Names**

**MAKE** a list of five cities and states. Make sure to **USE** commas correctly. (**LOOK** at page 250 in your handbook for help.) **SEE** page 306 in your handbook if you want to write five state capitals.

*Example:* Tallahassee, Florida

## Dear Mary, . . . . . . . . . . . . . . . . . Commas in Letters

**WRITE** a letter to a friend, telling all about your favorite animal. **PUT** commas after the greeting and the closing of your letter. If you need help, **LOOK** at page 250 in your handbook.

## Mr. Bear said . . . . . . . . Commas and Quotation Marks

**PRETEND** you can talk with a polar bear. **FILL IN** the blanks below. First **WRITE** what you think the bear would say. Then **WRITE** what you would say. **USE** quotation marks and commas correctly. If you need help, **LOOK** at pages 251 and 253 in your handbook.

Mr. Polar Bear said _____

_____

_____ .

_____

_____

_____ I answered.

## See You in the Funny Papers . . . . . . . . . . . . . . . . **Speakers' Words**

**DRAW** a comic strip (four frames long) of you and a friend having fun. **MAKE** speech balloons above your heads. **WRITE** the words you and your friend are saying to each other.

## Lunchtime! . . . . . . . . . . . **Punctuating Speakers' Words**

**IMAGINE** two ants talking about the good snacks they are eating from your picnic basket. **WRITE** the ants' words using quotation marks and other punctuation correctly. **SEE** pages 251 and 253 in your handbook for help.

## What did you write? . . . . . . . . . . . . . **Quotation Marks for Titles**

**OPEN** your writing folder. **PICK** your favorite story or poem. **WRITE** a sentence telling what you like best about it. **SEE** pages 253 and 256 in your handbook for help.

*Example:* I like my poem "Fun in the Summer" because it reminds me of my birthday.

## Two Thumbs Up! . . . . . . . . . . . . . . . **Underlining Titles**

**ASK** a partner two questions: (1) What is your favorite magazine? (2) What is your favorite book? Now **WRITE** two sentences: (1) Tell what your partner's favorite magazine is. (2) Tell what your partner's favorite book is. Be sure to capitalize and punctuate the titles correctly. **SEE** pages 253 and 256 in your handbook for help.

## Happy Birthday! . . . . . . . . . . . . . . . . . . . **Commas**

**ASK** three people to tell you what day they were born. **ASK** the year, too. **WRITE** down all the birthdays. Make sure to **USE** commas correctly. If you need help, **LOOK** on page 250 of your handbook.

## How big is it? . . . . . . . . . . . . . . . . . . . . . **Commas**

**OPEN** your handbook to page 307. **PICK** three facts about the United States, and **WRITE** a sentence for each one. Make sure you **INCLUDE** a number in each sentence, and **USE** a comma if needed.

*Example:* Alaska covers 586,412 square miles.

## One word was two words. ........... Apostrophes in Contractions

Below is a list of contractions. **COPY** the contractions. Don't forget the apostrophe. Then **WRITE** the two words that are used to make the contraction. **SEE** page 203 in your handbook.

| | Contraction | Two Words |
|---|---|---|
| 1. it's | it's | it is |
| 2. they're | _____ | _____ |
| 3. don't | _____ | _____ |
| 4. we've | _____ | _____ |
| 5. I'll | _____ | _____ |
| 6. I'm | _____ | _____ |

## Lost and Found .... Apostrophes to Show Ownership

**WRITE** words to show ownership for the list of nouns below. **SEE** page 252 in your handbook.

*Example:* the _____dog's_____ bone

1. _____ flowers     3. the _____ socks

2. the _____ wagon     4. _____ car

# Checking Mechanics Minilessons

---

Dear Uncle Mike, . . . . . . . . . . . . . . . . **Capital Letters**

---

**OPEN** your handbook to page 70. **READ** the note from Sarah to Uncle Mike. Now **PRETEND** Sarah is talking instead of writing. **FILL IN** the blanks below with Sarah's words. Use a capital letter for Sarah's first word in each sentence. **SEE** page 255 in your handbook for help.

1. Sarah said, " _Thank you for the calculator_ ."

2. Sarah said, " _____

   _____ !"

3. " _____

   _____ ," said Sarah.

---

I like holidays. . . . . . . . . . . . . . . . . . **Capital Letters**

---

**WRITE** sentences about two or three of your favorite holidays. **TELL** what you like best about each holiday. Be sure to **USE** capital letters correctly. **SEE** page 256 in your handbook.

*Example:* I love the heart cookies Grandma bakes for Valentine's Day.

## What's in a name? . . . . . . . . . . . . . . . **Capital Letters**

**LOOK** at the time line that begins on page 323 in your handbook. **PICK** three people from history. **WRITE** a sentence using each person's name. **USE** capital letters correctly.

## When I Grow Up . . . . . . . . . . . . . . . . **Capital Letters**

**WRITE** three sentences that begin with "When I grow up, I . . ." **THINK** of three things that you want to do or become. Always **USE** a capital "I" when you write about yourself.

## "Wet, Sunny Summer" . . . . . . . . . . . . **Capital Letters**

**PRETEND** you're going to write four poems—one for each season of the year: spring, summer, fall, and winter. **MAKE UP** titles for the poems. **WRITE** them on a piece of paper. **USE** capital letters and quotation marks correctly. **LOOK** at page 256 in your handbook if you need help.

## Today's the day. . . . . . . . . . . . . . . . . **Capital Letters**

**WRITE** three sentences. Each sentence should be about a different day of the week. Remember to **USE** capital letters for the days of the week.

*Example:* Every Saturday we go out for pizza.

## What month is it? . . . . . . . . . . . . . . . **Capital Letters**

**ANSWER** these questions. **BEGIN** each month with a capital letter.

1. What is the first month of the year? _____

2. In what month is your birthday? _____

3. In what month does school begin? _____

4. What is your favorite month? _____

## A Capital Idea . . . . . . . . . . . . . . . . . . **Capital Letters**

**MAKE UP** some new holidays, like Ice Cream Day or Puppy Day. **WRITE** down the names of your holidays, and remember to **USE** capital letters correctly.

## Use capitals for capitals. . . . . . . . . **Capital Letters**

**WRITE** down the name of the capital of your state. If you need help, **LOOK** at page 306 in your handbook. Now **LOOK** at the map on page 305. **FIND** two states that are next to your state. **WRITE** the names of their capitals. Make sure you begin each capital city with a capital letter!

## Lots of Helpers . . . . . . . . . . . . . . . . **Plurals Using "s"**

**FIND** the names of four community helpers on page 287 in your handbook. **WRITE** their names on a piece of paper. Next to each name, **WRITE** its plural form. **CHECK** the rules for forming plurals on page 257.

*Example:* police officer – police officers

## That's silly! . . . . . . . . . . . . . . . . . **Plurals Using "es"**

**READ** the list of eight words below. **PICK** two of the words. **CHANGE** them to plurals, and **USE** them in a sentence. **DO** the same thing again, using two different words. **SEE** the rules about plurals on page 257. Make your sentences as silly as you can!

*Example:* The two foxes ate 100 lunches.

**brush   lunch   class   fox   buzz   bunch   dish   box**

## Help! . . . . . . . . . . . . . . . . **Plurals That Change the Word**

**READ** the sentences below.  The writer forgot to use plurals!
**WRITE** the correct plural word in each blank.  (See page
59 in your SourceBook if you need help.)

Two _____children_____ saw three _____
(child)                          (goose)

scare the four _____ .  The _____
(mouse)                          (man)

jumped to their _____ when three
(foot)

_____ ran by.
(wolf)

## Y and Y Not . . . . . . . . . . . **Plurals: Words Ending in "y"**

**OPEN** your handbook to page 287.  **FIND** every word on the
page that ends in "y." *Hint:* Don't forget to look at the
heading.  **WRITE** each word as a plural.  If you need help,
**LOOK** at page 257 in your handbook.

_____

_____

_____

*Checking Mechanics Minilessons*    **115**

## Mr. Me . . . . . . . . . . . . . . . . . . . . . . . . . . . . . . **Abbreviations**

We usually call grown-ups by their titles, like Mr., Ms., or Mrs. On a piece of paper, **WRITE** your name and the name of your best friend. Add the titles you will be called when you are grown-ups. Now **WRITE** your names again, this time using the title you both will have if you become doctors. **SEE** page 258 in your handbook for help.

*Example:* Ms. Laura Banks, Dr. Laura Banks

## Dear Me, . . . . . . . . . . . . . . . . . . . . . . . **Addresses**

**PRETEND** you are writing a letter to yourself. **WRITE** your address as you would write it on an envelope. **USE** all capitals and no punctuation. **LOOK** at page 258 in your handbook for help.

## Dear Mr. President, . . . . . . . . . . . . . . . . . . . **Addresses**

**PRETEND** you're writing a letter to the president of the United States. Here is his address: 1600 Pennsylvania Avenue, Washington, DC 20500. **WRITE** the address as if you were putting it on an envelope. **LOOK** at page 258 in your handbook for help.

# Using the Right Word Minilessons

How many legs does
your aunt have? . . . . . . . . . . . . . **Using the Right Word**

**TURN** to pages 268 and 269 of your handbook. **PICK** one set
of words. **READ** the example sentences. On a piece of
paper, **COPY** the sentences, but switch the words.

*Example:* An <u>aunt</u> crawled onto my finger.

My <u>ant</u> likes to tell jokes.

(These sentences are silly, aren't they?)

**ASK** a friend to read and correct your silly sentences.

I had four pancakes
for breakfast. . . . . . . . . . . . . . **Using the Right Word**

**OPEN** your handbook to page 269. **PICK** one set of words
from the page. **WRITE** one sentence that uses both words
correctly.

*Example:* I held a baby <u>bear</u> in my <u>bare</u> hands.

Now **PICK** another set of words. **WRITE** a sentence using
both of those words correctly.

## Hear, Here . . . . . . . . . . . . . . . . **Using the Right Word**

**WORK** with a partner. **OPEN** your handbook to pages 270 and 271. **PICK** a set of words, but don't let your partner see. **READ** the first word and sentence out loud to your partner.

*Example:* "Hear—I like to hear birds sing."

**ASK** your partner to write down the word. Then check it. Take turns.

## Spell Down . . . . . . . . . . . . . . . . **Using the Right Word**

With a partner, **OPEN** your handbook to page 272. Have your partner **READ** the first word *(sew)* and the example sentence out loud. Then you may **SPELL** the word out loud, without looking. Your partner will tell you whether you are right or wrong. Let your partner read all the sentences on page 272 in this same way. Each time, you spell the word.

Next, **YOU READ** the words and sentences on page 273, so your partner can practice spelling.

# Checking Your Sentences
# Minilessons

---

## S or V .................. Adding Subjects or Verbs

---

**TURN** to page 274 in your handbook. **COMPLETE** the
following simple sentences. **ADD** a subject or a verb,
whichever is needed.

1. _____ swim.      4. Cars _____ .

2. _____ hurry.     5. Parrots _____ .

3. Children _____ .  6. _____ shines.

---

## Season Sentences ........... Complete Sentences

---

**TURN** to page 285 in your handbook. **LOOK** at the list of
season/weather words. **PICK** two of the words, and
**WRITE** one sentence using both of them.

*Example:* It is <u>cold</u> in the <u>winter</u>.

## Tell me a game. . . . . . . . . . . . . . . . . . **Telling Sentences**

What is your favorite game?  On a piece of paper, **FINISH**
this telling sentence:

I like to play _____ .

Now **WRITE** two more telling sentences.  Tell what you like
about the game.

## The 5 W's . . . . . . . . . . . . . . . . . . . . . . . **Asking Sentences**

**WRITE** five simple questions a partner could answer.  **BEGIN**
each question with one of the 5 W's.  Who . . . ?
What . . . ?  When . . . ?  Where . . . ?  Why . . . ?

*Example:*  Who was the first president?

## You're the cat's meow!  . . . . **Exclamatory Sentences**

**TURN** to page 132 in your handbook.  **READ** the story.
**COUNT** the exclamatory sentences you find.  How many
are there?  Now **WRITE** two of your own exclamatory
sentences about a kitten.  Check your punctuation.  **SEE**
page 275 in your handbook for help.

# Understanding Our Language Minilessons

---

## How many nouns? . . . . . . . . . . . . . . . . . . . . . . **Nouns**

---

**OPEN** your handbook to page 277 and **READ** about nouns.
Next, **READ** the paragraph about the bus on page 127.
On a piece of paper, **WRITE** down all the nouns you find
in the paragraph. (There are seven nouns in all. Some
are singular, and some are plural.)

---

## Person, Place, Thing . . . . . . . . . . . . . . . **Plural Nouns**

---

**WRITE** down three nouns that name things. Now **WRITE** the
plural of each noun. Finally, **WRITE** a silly sentence
using all three plural nouns. **SEE** pages 257 and 277 in
your handbook for help.

---

## Not Just Any Old Park . . . . . . . . . . . . . . **Proper Nouns**

---

**OPEN** your handbook to page 60. **READ** the story about
visiting the park. On the lines below, **WRITE** each proper
noun you find in the story. **SEE** page 277 in your
handbook for help.

_____

_____

## Is that mine? . . . . . . . . . . . . . . . . . . Possessive Nouns

**CHOOSE** three things in your classroom that belong to three different people. On a piece of paper, **WRITE** a sentence that begins with "That is . . ."

*Example:* That is my teacher's desk.

Now **WRITE** sentences for the three things you chose. **SEE** page 277 in your handbook for help.

## Starring: You! . . . . . . . . . . . . . . . . . . Pronouns

Here is a paragraph from a story. Pretend that you are Aladdin. **REWRITE** the paragraph on a piece of paper, changing each underlined word to "I," "my," or "me."

Aladdin jumped out the window. He caught his coat on the edge of the building. He dangled over the street. The flying carpet swooped up to save him, and he soared into the sky.

## He said I could keep it. . . . . . . . . . . . . . . **Pronouns**

**TURN** to page 220 in your handbook. **READ** the story about the yellow elephant. Below is a list of pronouns that are in the story. Next to each pronoun, **WRITE** the number of times you find that pronoun in the story.

1. **his** _____     5. **me** _____

2. **he** _____     6. **they** _____

3. **it** _____     7. **I** _____

4. **my** _____     8. **you** _____

## It's an elephant. . . . . . . . . . . . . . . . . . . **Pronouns**

Do this minilesson with a partner. **OPEN** your handbook to page 223. **READ** the second part of the story about a yellow elephant. On a piece of paper, **WRITE** down the six different pronouns you see in the story.

## Play, Play, Play . . . . . . . . . . . . . . . . . . . **Verbs**

**CHOOSE** three things you really like to do. **WRITE** a sentence about each thing. **UNDERLINE** the verb in each sentence. **SEE** page 279 in your handbook for help.

*Example:* I <u>chase</u> my dog down the street.

*Understanding Our Language Minilessons*    **123**

## The History of You . . . . . . . . . . . . **Past Tense Verbs**

**THINK** of three things you did yesterday. On a piece of paper, **WRITE** three sentences telling what you did. **USE** past tense verbs. **UNDERLINE** the verb in each sentence. **SEE** page 279 in your handbook for help.

*Example:* I <u>played</u> soccer.

## Planning Ahead . . . . . . . . . . . . . . **Future Tense Verbs**

Pretend that you can do anything you want to do tomorrow. **WRITE** three sentences telling what you will do. **USE** future tense verbs. **UNDERLINE** the verb in each sentence. **SEE** page 279 in your handbook for help.

*Example:* I <u>will ride</u> roller coasters all morning.

## Help Again! . . . . . . . . . . . . . . . . . **Irregular Verbs**

The two sentences below have irregular verbs. But the writer used them like regular verbs. **REWRITE** the sentences on your own paper. **CHANGE** the underlined verbs to the correct words. **LOOK** at page 281 in your handbook for help.

Billy <u>runned</u> to play with Freddy after he <u>eated</u> lunch.

Maria <u>drawed</u> a picture to give to her mom and <u>hided</u> it until her birthday.

## I Do, I Did . . . . . . . . . . . . . . . . . . . . **Irregular Verbs**

**OPEN** your handbook to page 281.  **PICK** one of the irregular verbs.  On a piece of paper, **WRITE** a sentence using the present tense form of the verb you picked.  Then **WRITE** the sentence again, changing it to past tense.

*Example:* Every day I give my guinea pig lettuce.

Yesterday I gave my guinea pig lettuce.

Now **PICK** another irregular verb.  **WRITE** two more sentences.

## How does it feel? . . . . . . . . . . . . . . . . . **Adjectives**

Some adjectives describe how something feels.  **SEE** how many different "feeling" adjectives you can **WRITE** to **DESCRIBE** these words.  You might want to feel these things before you write your words!

| WIND | SWEATER | SIDEWALK |
| --- | --- | --- |
| _____ | _____ | _____ |
| _____ | _____ | _____ |
| _____ | _____ | _____ |
| _____ | _____ | _____ |
| _____ | _____ | _____ |

*Understanding Our Language Minilessons*

## Cheerful Birthday to You! . . . . . . . . . . . . **Adjectives**

Next time you say "happy birthday" to someone, **TRY** to find a new way to say it. The word "happy" is an adjective, but there are many other words that have a similar meaning.

**LIST** as many words as you can that mean "happy." The next time you make a birthday card, you may want to try one of your new adjectives.

*Examples:* cheerful, hilarious

## Smarter Than the Average Bear . . . . . . . **Adjectives**

Are you smaller than an elephant? Are you bigger than an ant? **WRITE** two sentences that compare you with something else. **USE** adjectives that compare things. **SEE** page 282 in your handbook for help with adjectives that compare.

*Examples:* bigger, taller, smaller, smarter

# Using Theme Words Minilessons

---

## January is cold and snowy. . . . . . . . . Days/Months

**OPEN** your handbook to page 284. **LOOK** over the words for days and months. **CHOOSE** a day and **WRITE** a sentence about it. Then choose a month and write a sentence about it.

---

## Wednesday is hardest! . . . . . . . . . . . Days/Months

Do this minilesson with a partner. **OPEN** your handbook to page 284. **PRACTICE** saying the days of the week in order, without looking. (Your partner can look at the handbook to see if you are right.)

After you can say them, **LEARN** to spell them. As your partner calls out each day of the week, **WRITE** the word. Then **CHECK** your work. For a real challenge, learn to say and spell the months of the year, too!

---

## Doctor, Plumber, Firefighter . . . . Community Words

**TURN** to page 287 in your handbook. **LOOK** over the community words. **MAKE** a list of five community helpers. Then **WRITE** a sentence about each helper.

## Food Sort . . . . . . . . . . . . . . . . . . . . . . . . . . **Food Words**

**TURN** to page 286 in your handbook. **READ** the food words. Then make three columns on a piece of paper. Name the columns: Yummy, So-So, and Yuck. **WRITE** each food word in the column of your choice. **COMPARE** your lists with others in your class.

| Yummy | So-So | Yuck |
|-------|-------|------|
|       |       |      |
|       |       |      |

## It was a dark and sunny night. . . . . . . . . . . **Season/Weather Words**

**LOOK** over the season/weather words on page 285 in your handbook. On a piece of paper, **WRITE** some nonsense sentences using some of these words. ("Nonsense" means something that doesn't make sense!)

*Example:* Winter finally came! It was hot and sunny. There were clouds on the ground.

# MUG Shot Sentences

These MUG Shot Sentences review basic writing skills—mechanics, usage, and grammar. They provide daily practice with proofreading skills.

# Focused
# SENTENCES

✱ Periods - At the End of a Telling Sentence

I like to cook with my dad

✱ Periods - At the End of a Telling Sentence

He makes the best blueberry pancakes

✱ Periods - At the End of a Telling Sentence

My job is to add the flour to the bowl

✱ Periods - At the End of a Telling Sentence

Sometimes Dad lets me break an egg

✱ Periods - At the End of a Telling Sentence

We have fun making pancake men together

# Focused SENTENCES

* Periods - After an Abbreviation

Our music teacher is Mrs Davis.

* Periods - After an Abbreviation

Mom took Ben to see Dr Adams.

* Periods - After an Abbreviation

Mrs Beasley is a kind principal.

* Periods - After an Abbreviation

Mr Rogers lives across the street from us.

* Periods - After an Abbreviation

Our gym teacher is Ms Ryan.

# Focused
# SENTENCES

* Periods - Between Dollars and Cents

I get $ 1 0 0 each week for my allowance.

* Periods - Between Dollars and Cents

My sister has $ 3 4 5 in her wallet.

* Periods - Between Dollars and Cents

Mom said the puzzle cost $ 2 5 0.

* Periods - Between Dollars and Cents

I loaned $ 4 2 5 to my brother.

* Periods - Between Dollars and Cents

Joey's bike cost $ 5 6 0 0!

# Focused
# SENTENCES

✱ **Question Marks - After a Question**

How many continents are there

✱ Question Marks - After a Question

What is the biggest lake in this country

✱ Question Marks - After a Question

When will the United States be 300 years old

✱ Question Marks - After a Question

Are nickels bigger than dimes

✱ **Question Marks - After a Question**

Who wrote <u>Little House in the Big Woods</u>

# Focused
# SENTENCES

* **Exclamation Points - After a Sentence**

Look at that catch

* **Exclamation Points - After a Sentence**

The catcher banged into the wall

* **Exclamation Points - After a Sentence**

Now our team is up to bat

* **Exclamation Points - After a Sentence**

Amazing Austin will save the day

* **Exclamation Points - After a Sentence**

Oh no, he struck out

# Focused SENTENCES

* Commas - Between a City and a State

Katie lives in Milford Michigan.

* Commas - Between a City and a State

Disney World is in Orlando Florida.

* Commas - Between a City and a State

Annie can't wait to go to San Antonio Texas.

* Commas - Between a City and a State

Would you like to visit Friendly West Virginia?

* Commas - Between a City and a State

Do many writers live in Pencil Bluff Arkansas?

# Focused
# SENTENCES

* **Commas - Between the Day and the Year**

My brother was born on March 15 1995.

* **Commas - Between the Day and the Year**

Our family will go on vacation June 14 1997.

* **Commas - Between the Day and the Year**

On July 4 1996, the U.S.A. was 220 years old.

* **Commas - Between the Day and the Year**

On March 21 2000, Regan will be 10 years old.

* **Commas - Between the Day and the Year**

The next leap year day is February 29 2000.

*MUG Shot Sentences*

# Focused
# SENTENCES

* **Commas - After the Greeting and the Closing in a Letter**

Dear Aunt Sue

   Thank you for my new sweater.   The stripes are cool.   I wore it to school today.

                Love

                Benji

* **Commas - After the Greeting and the Closing in a Letter**

Dear Grandma Diane

   Will you come to my tea party?   It's on Saturday at 11:00.   I will serve sugar cookies. I hope you can come!

                Your granddaughter

                Kathryn

# Focused
# SENTENCES

**✱ Commas - Between Words in a Series**

Wyoming Utah and Idaho are western states.

**✱ Commas - Between Words in a Series**

Hawaii is warm sunny and beautiful.

**✱ Commas - Between Words in a Series**

I can swim skate and fish in Minnesota.

**✱ Commas - Between Words in a Series**

Florida Alabama and Georgia are in the South.

**✱ Commas - Between Words in a Series**

Cherries apples and peaches grow in Michigan.

*MUG Shot Sentences*    **139**

# Focused
# SENTENCES

* Commas - To Keep Big Numbers Clear

A new car can cost $ 2 0 0 0 0 dollars.

* Commas - To Keep Big Numbers Clear

There are 3 2 0 0 0 ounces in a ton.

* Commas - To Keep Big Numbers Clear

New York City has 7 0 0 0 0 0 0 people.

* Commas - To Keep Big Numbers Clear

A mile is 5 2 8 0 feet long.

* Commas - To Keep Big Numbers Clear

It's 2 4 9 0 2 miles around the earth.

# Focused
# SENTENCES

✳ Commas - To Help Set Off a Speaker's Words

Mrs. Frazzle called "It's time for gym."

✳ Commas - To Help Set Off a Speaker's Words

"After gym, we can have a treat " said Mike.

✳ Commas - To Help Set Off a Speaker's Words

Joshua asked "What treat did you bring?"

✳ Commas - To Help Set Off a Speaker's Words

"It's a surprise " Michael answered.

✳ Commas - To Help Set Off a Speaker's Words

Suzie whispered "I can't wait to find out!"

# Focused
# SENTENCES

* Apostrophes - To Make a Contraction

  Mr. Wallace hasnt checked our tests yet.

* Apostrophes - To Make a Contraction

  I dont think I made any mistakes.

* Apostrophes - To Make a Contraction

  Well get our spelling tests back after lunch.

* Apostrophes - To Make a Contraction

  Maria cant find her spelling book.

* Apostrophes - To Make a Contraction

  She wasnt sure how to spell "house."

# Focused
# SENTENCES

✱ Apostrophes - To Show That Someone Owns Something

My familys favorite drive-in sells ice cream.

✱ Apostrophes - To Show That Someone Owns Something

Lemon cheesecake is Jannas favorite flavor.

✱ Apostrophes - To Show That Someone Owns Something

Mint chocolate chip is Moms favorite flavor.

✱ Apostrophes - To Show That Someone Owns Something

My sisters favorite flavor is cherry.

✱ Apostrophes - To Show That Someone Owns Something

I always taste Grandpas banana split.

# Focused
# SENTENCES

* Apostrophes - To Show That Someone Owns Something

The three girls clothes got wet in the rain.

* Apostrophes - To Show That Someone Owns Something

Both parents cars were parked in the street.

* Apostrophes - To Show That Someone Owns Something

My teachers names are Mr. Ian and Ms. Rose.

* Apostrophes - To Show That Someone Owns Something

The two boys dog is a cocker spaniel.

* Apostrophes - To Show That Someone Owns Something

Our pets names are Bambino and Bobber.

# Focused
# SENTENCES

* **Quotation Marks - Before and After a Speaker's Words**

Grandpa fixed your bike, Mom said.

* **Quotation Marks - Before and After a Speaker's Words**

Thank you, Gramps! I cried.

* **Quotation Marks - Before and After a Speaker's Words**

The back tire was bent, explained Grandpa.

* **Quotation Marks - Before and After a Speaker's Words**

I hugged him and said, You're the best!

* **Quotation Marks - Before and After a Speaker's Words**

Take it for a ride, Grandpa said.

# Focused
# SENTENCES

* **Underlining - For Titles of Books and Magazines**

We get Spider magazine at our house.

* **Underlining - For Titles of Books and Magazines**

The Little House is my favorite book.

* **Underlining - For Titles of Books and Magazines**

Did you read the book When I Get Bigger?

* **Underlining - For Titles of Books and Magazines**

My little brother loves Ladybug magazine.

* **Underlining - For Titles of Books and Magazines**

We read Highlights magazines at the library.

# Focused SENTENCES

**✷ Capital Letters - For the First Word in a Sentence**

our read-aloud book is called <u>The Chalk Box Kid</u>.

**✷ Capital Letters - For the First Word in a Sentence**

i love getting letters in the mail.

**✷ Capital Letters - For the First Word in a Sentence**

"do you like to swim in the ocean?" he asked.

**✷ Capital Letters - For the First Word in a Sentence**

mrs. Lambert is my favorite neighbor.

**✷ Capital Letters - For the First Word in a Sentence**

the highest mountain I've seen is in Alaska.

# Focused SENTENCES

* Capital Letters - For a Speaker's First Word

Mr. Brown said, "your handwriting is neat."

* Capital Letters - For a Speaker's First Word

I said, "thank you!"

* Capital Letters - For a Speaker's First Word

"can you make a sign for our door?" he asked.

* Capital Letters - For a Speaker's First Word

"what should the sign say?" I asked.

* Capital Letters - For a Speaker's First Word

Mr. Brown answered, "welcome to our class."

# Focused
# SENTENCES

✱ Capital Letters - For Names and Titles

lavon raced billy joe to the playground.

✱ Capital Letters - For Names and Titles

John price and peter mann played catch.

✱ Capital Letters - For Names and Titles

We played kickball with mr. meyer's class.

✱ Capital Letters - For Names and Titles

mrs. kelly blew her whistle three times.

✱ Capital Letters - For Names and Titles

julie called, "It's time to line up now!"

# Focused
# SENTENCES

* Capital Letters - For the Word "I"

One thing i enjoy is collecting seashells.

* Capital Letters - For the Word "I"

i like the scallops, tulips, and buttercups.

* Capital Letters - For the Word "I"

It's important to use sunscreen when i go shelling.

* Capital Letters - For the Word "I"

Sometimes i find shells buried in the sand.

* Capital Letters - For the Word "I"

Once i found a big sea biscuit while snorkeling.

# Focused
# SENTENCES

* **Capital Letters - For Titles of Books, Stories, Poems, . . .**

Karen and I read <u>stone soup</u> together.

* **Capital Letters - For Titles of Books, Stories, Poems, . . .**

I made a poster for <u>ira sleeps over</u>.

* **Capital Letters - For Titles of Books, Stories, Poems, . . .**

<u>Little house on the prairie</u> is a great book.

* **Capital Letters - For Titles of Books, Stories, Poems, . . .**

Bryce read <u>boxcar children</u> last week.

* **Capital Letters - For Titles of Books, Stories, Poems, . . .**

Mrs. Perez is reading <u>stone fox</u> to us.

*MUG Shot Sentences*   **151**

# Focused
# SENTENCES

* **Capital Letters - For Days, Months, and Holidays**

We had a valentine's day party in february.

* **Capital Letters - For Days, Months, and Holidays**

Memorial day is always on a monday.

* **Capital Letters - For Days, Months, and Holidays**

We will do our book reports on wednesday.

* **Capital Letters - For Days, Months, and Holidays**

In june we will have a storybook parade!

* **Capital Letters - For Days, Months, and Holidays**

This september we will be in second grade!

# Focused
# SENTENCES

✳ **Capital Letters - For Names of Places**

Our family wants to visit the grand canyon.

✳ **Capital Letters - For Names of Places**

The grand canyon is in arizona.

✳ **Capital Letters - For Names of Places**

We'll drive through texas and new mexico.

✳ **Capital Letters - For Names of Places**

I hope we will see the rio grande river.

✳ **Capital Letters - For Names of Places**

We'll go through colorado on our way home.

# Focused SENTENCES

✳ Making Plurals - Add "s"

Megan made a picnic for her three sister.

✳ Making Plurals - Add "es"

Sydney ate bunchs of grapes.

✳ Making Plurals - Add "es"

Alexis liked the peanut butter sandwichs.

✳ Making Plurals - Add "s"

Marissa drank two bottle of juice.

✳ Making Plurals - Add "es"

Megan was happy they liked their lunchs.

**154**  *MUG Shot Sentences*

# Focused
# SENTENCES

✱ **Using the Right Word**

Did you here that train whistle?


✱ **Using the Right Word**

The train goes by at for o'clock each day.


✱ **Using the Right Word**

Susan saw the train this time, but eye didn't.


✱ **Using the Right Word**

I wonder wear it is going today.


✱ **Using the Right Word**

Johnny wood like to be a conductor someday.

# Focused
# SENTENCES

✱ **Using the Right Word**

Our cousins came to sea us at Thanksgiving.


✱ **Using the Right Word**

Mom served to kinds of meat for dinner.


✱ **Using the Right Word**

Ant Janie read us some stories after dessert.


✱ **Using the Right Word**

I love the one about the son and the wind.


✱ **Using the Right Word**

Grandma blue kisses to everyone.

# Focused
# SENTENCES

✱ Using the Right Word

Karen likes to read fairy tails.

✱ Using the Right Word

<u>Sleeping Beauty</u> is won of her favorites.

✱ Using the Right Word

What is you're favorite storybook?

✱ Using the Right Word

Joseph new <u>Rumpelstiltskin</u> by heart.

✱ Using the Right Word

My too favorites are <u>Cinderella</u> and <u>Aladdin</u>.

# Proofreading
# SENTENCES

## Penguins

✱ **Capitalization, Using the Right Word**

penguin fathers warm the eggs on there feet.

✱ **Capitalization, Apostrophes**

most penguins babies hatch in about 55 days.

✱ **Apostrophes, Using the Right Word**

At first, the babies dont look like they're parents.

✱ **Capitalization, Commas in a Series**

they are brown soft and cute.

✱ **Capitalization, Apostrophes**

after a year, penguins feathers are waterproof.

# Proofreading
# SENTENCES

## Zebras

✱ Capitalization, End Punctuation

zebras live in large herds in africa

✱ Commas, Quotation Marks

Grandpa said Baby zebras weigh about 70 pounds.

✱ Quotation Marks, Capitalization

they are called foals, the zookeeper added.

✱ Apostrophes, End Punctuation

Each zebras stripes form a different pattern

✱ Using the Right Word, End Punctuation

Do zebras have brown hare on their backs

# Proofreading
# SENTENCES

## Storms

✳ Capitalization, Commas in a Series

lightning is quick surprising and dangerous.

✳ Apostrophes, End Punctuation

Dont play outside when you see lightning

✳ Apostrophes, End Punctuation

Johnnys puppy doesnt like the sound of thunder

✳ Capitalization, Commas in a Series

she whines cries and shakes until John pets her.

✳ Apostrophes, Using the Right Word

Annies mom loves to here rain on the roof.

*MUG Shot Sentences*

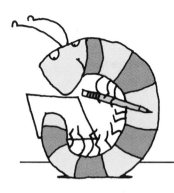

# Proofreading
## SENTENCES

### Tornadoes

✱ Capitalization, End Punctuation

a tornado can cause a lot of damage

✱ Capitalization, End Punctuation

its funnel acts like a giant vacuum cleaner

✱ Capitalization, Commas in a Series

tornadoes can pick up trees cars and houses!

✱ Capitalization, Using the Right Word

it maid a flat path through Grandpa's woulds!

✱ Using the Right Word, Capitalization

My ant saw a tornado in oklahoma.

# Proofreading SENTENCES

## Seashore

**✷ Apostrophes, End Punctuation**

A hermit crabs body is four inches long

**✷ Apostrophes, End Punctuation**

Can a lizards tail be longer than its body

**✷ Capitalization, End Punctuation**

oystercatcher birds live on the shores of india

**✷ Apostrophes, End Punctuation**

Is an oystercatchers bill wedge shaped

**✷ Quotation Marks, Underlining Titles**

She said, Read The Seashore to learn about oceans.

*MUG Shot Sentences*   **163**

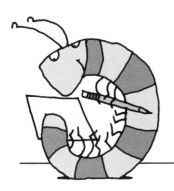

# Proofreading
# SENTENCES

**Frogs**

✱ End Punctuation, Commas in a Series

Dear Kevin,

I'm sending you a picture of my new pet frog He is so cool His name is Fido, and he's a leopard frog I feed him worms spiders and bugs

Write back soon

Your friend,

Robby

# **Proofreading**
## SENTENCES

### Caves

✱ Commas in Letters, Capitalization

Dear robby

    We're in kentucky! Yesterday we explored mammoth cave. the cave was cool, dark, and spooky. mom and emily didn't like the beetles. i thought they were neat. Did you know that eyeless fish and blind insects live in the cave?

       Your friend

       Kevin

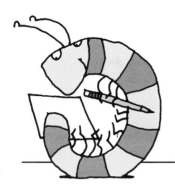

# Proofreading
# SENTENCES

## Bridges

* **Periods Between Dollars and Cents, Capitalization**

It costs $ 3 0 0 to cross the fort myers Bridge.

* **Capitalization, End Punctuation**

The famous london bridge had 19 arches

* **Apostrophes, Capitalization**

Londons Tower bridge is a moving bridge!

* **Capitalization, Using the Right Word**

it takes for minutes two raise the drawbridge.

* **Capitalization, End Punctuation**

the Chesapeake bay Bridge has two tunnels

# Proofreading SENTENCES

## Tunnels

✱ **Quotation Marks, Periods After an Abbreviation**

Mrs Evans, do tunnels scare you?  I asked.

✱ **Using the Right Word, End Punctuation**

Tunnels go through mountains and under sees

✱ **Commas in a Series, Using the Right Word**

Earthworms moles and aunts make tunnels.

✱ **Periods After an Abbreviation, End Punctuation**

Mr Mill asked, "Where is Windsor Tunnel "

✱ **Quotation Marks, Exclamation Points**

Joe yelled, Wow We drove under the river

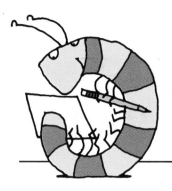

# Proofreading
## SENTENCES

### Mammals

* **Capitalization, End Punctuation**

  In <u>All About mammals</u> we read about whales

* **Capitalization, Commas in Dates**

  We went to the national zoo on june 17 1995.

* **Commas in a Series, Apostrophes**

  The gorillas lions and bears werent very active.

* **Apostrophes, End Punctuation**

  When its hot, big mammals rest a lot

* **Capitalization, Periods After an Abbreviation**

  "In october, the lions are playful," said Dr Sym.